Gifts of the Heart

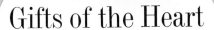

Gifts of the Heart

by Dean Walley

Illustrated by
Thelma Christensen

HALLMARK EDITIONS

Gifts of the Heart

Gold and silver are gifts

That are treasured by many...

But the gifts
of the heart
Cost not a penny.

A smile is a gift
You can give every day.

A letter's a gift
To a friend
who's away.

Laughter's a gift

That holds happiness in it.

Time is a gift
To enjoy
every minute.

Some people like
The gift of advice.

It's a gift
just to say
"I like you!
You're nice!"

A quarrel patched up

is a special gift . . .

And so is giving
Someone a lift.

A task is a gift

That can even be fun . . .

And praise
is a gift
For a task well done.

"Thank you's" and "Pleases"
And "Yes'es" are gifts,

But seldom give
"Oh no's"
Or "Maybe's"
or "If's."

We sometimes find gifts
In the strangest of places—
Like old trunks . . .

And old trees . . .

And very shy faces.

The world is a gift,
For God, in His love,
Gives us green meadows
And blue skies above.

Giving's receiving,
Receiving is giving!
That's really the secret
That lies behind living.

So give something
each day
And you'll find
that it's true...

All the gifts of the heart
Will be given to you.